OTIS

Memoir of a
Privileged King Charles Spaniel

Also by Babette Williams

Dancing in High Cotton

OTIS

Memoir of a Privileged King Charles Spaniel

Translated into People-Speak
by
Babette Williams

www.BabetteWilliams.com
Babette007@aol.com

"Otis: Memoir of a Privileged King Charles Spaniel ," by Babette Williams.
ISBN 1-58939-862-9.

Published 2006 by Virtualbookworm.com Publishing Inc., P.O. Box 9949, College Station, TX 77842, US.

Manufactured in the United States of America.

TO MY ADOPTIVE PARENTS

ELLEN AND STEVE SUSMAN

Who recognize quality when they see it —

I love you,

Otis

Chapter One

My name is Otis, I'm a dog, and I love to fly.

Actually, Otis isn't my real name, but that's what everybody calls me. My given name — the one on my impeccable pedigree — is Sonesta's Putting on the Ritz, yet I like Otis better. I wonder: When I was a puppy, how could anyone have known that I'd frequently stay at the Ritz?

I know that spaniels don't fly, but I'm different. As a matter of record, I've had my own private jet as long as I can remember. Not only that: I have my own two pilots, Jim and Gerald. They love me and let me steer the plane. The last time we landed at JFK Airport I was sitting in Jim's lap as we taxied to the hangar.

Suddenly an excited voice screamed through the mike, "Come look at this! A dog is landing that jet."

I love making history.

From the day I was born, I knew I was destined for high places. Something deep in my heart kept assuring me that I was meant to lead an exciting, adventurous life.

Now here I am, an ordinary Cavalier King Charles Spaniel, fulfilling my destiny. That is, if you can say any King Charles Spaniel is ordinary.

Everyone says I'm handsome. Even if it sounds a bit conceited, I think so too. I'm a tri-color—my silky coat is black and white, tinged with brown highlights. Like all Cavaliers, I have a plumed tail that I wave constantly. My father is a great champion. His name is Ralph Lauren. The famous clothing line is probably named after him.

My first clear memories are of playing with my sister, Classy, in a square pen lodged against one wall of an airy, sunlit room. My mother (or dam, as they say in dog language) is a warm and ever-present body. I love the feel of her silky coat, especially when I nuzzle against her side for a big drink of milk. Her large, round, dark brown eyes watch me tenderly—boy, do I feel loved and comfortable.

A gray-haired lady with sparkling blue eyes is always there catering to our needs.

I don't know it yet, but we live on a farm just outside Houston, Texas.

One day our mom has a heart-to-heart talk with Classy and me.

"Now that you're two months old, the time has come for you to be 'adopted' by a human. I have my very own human—the lady that takes care of us every day—but you each will find your special human."

Classy and I act a bit puzzled, so our mom explains more clearly.

"You see, I'm going to stay right here with my special human, but soon you'll both be leaving. You must promise me never to forget your heritage and to be proud of the fact that the late Queen Mother of England loved Cavalier King Charles Spaniels. You have royalty in your blood. Cavaliers have been bred for centuries as companion dogs for the aristocracy. Sometimes humans even refer to us as 'The Ultimate Snob Dog.'"

I don't know who the Queen Mother is, though I try to understand. Maybe I'll get it later on. Meanwhile, I don't like the idea of leaving my own mother.

"We're going to have lots of visitors during the next few weeks," she continues, "people wanting to adopt a puppy. When you are chosen, you'll leave here and go to a new home. Remember, when things get rough and confusing, that change is necessary and inevitable."

Now I truly don't know what she's talking about. What kind of changes? What will life be like without my mom and Classy? This is getting scary! Now my mom has more to say.

"Pay close attention, for this is the most important part. Each of you can be anything you choose to be. Of course environment is important to good development, but I know my human will choose a good home for you. Oh—just one more thing: Try to be your most charming self when the people visit. It's vital to be adorable."

It was only much later, when I came back to visit my mother, that I understood how far I had climbed. To be precise, I now reside on the twenty-third floor of The Huntingdon, Houston's most prestigious residence. That's about as high as you can climb in Texas.

Chapter Two

One lady has come to see us several times. She must be an owner-person, a human. I think she likes me the best. She talks a lot and I'm not certain what she's saying, but she smells nice and her touch is soft and kind. Maybe she's my destiny. I hope so.

There's a distinct scent wafting towards the kennel—I think that lady's here again. Wow! Isn't she pretty! She looks just the way she smells, which is good, good, and very good. I'm going to wag my tail extra hard. She's about to pick me up. Oh, I like this!

The lady's scent is so pleasant that I waggle my whole body until my silky coat presses tightly against her. At the same time I gaze up into her face. I am truly adorable. We are bonding.

"Well, what do you think?" Madame Blue-Eyes asks Mrs. Smell-So-Good.

"This little puppy is adorable," she coos. "He has the most beautiful, expressive, brown eyes. But there's just one problem: I'm concerned about my husband's reaction. You see, he's never had a dog, or any sort of pet for that matter, and he's not positive about adopting a puppy. We travel a great deal, which is another complication."

"Why don't you take the puppy home for a few days and see how it goes," suggests my mother's human. "If it doesn't work out, just bring him back. He's such a good little fellow, we'll have no difficulty finding him another home."

There is a long pause. A very long pause. I hold my breath and roll my eyes, not daring to move a muscle. Then Mrs. Smell-So-Good nods and says, "It's done. Let's give it a try."

I have been adopted. I am the first one to leave home.

Bye, Classy. I love you.

Chapter Three

Mrs. Smell-So-Good carries me outside. We are leaving my mom and Classy. She holds me tight and talks to me non-stop.

"Now don't worry, it's going to be all right," she croons. "We're going home and you'll meet Steve and we'll give you a name. You'll have toys, a bowl for food, another bowl for water, and you'll meet Herman and Lucy."

The splendid part is she's petting me all this time. The bad news is I really don't follow much of what she's saying.

Now she's opening the door of a square box and we get in. She puts me next to her, and the next thing I know there's a roaring feeling and we're moving. Is this my new home? I like the motion and fall asleep, dreaming about the future.

Suddenly the motion stops and I wake up.

A man opens the door to the box we're in.

"Good day, Mrs. Susman," he says, smiling politely. "Shall I park the car?"

Then he notices me and adds, "Oh, what have we here?"

Surely he knows I'm a dog? It doesn't matter—he reaches out to pet me. Following my mother's instruction to remember that King Charles Spaniels have a reputation to uphold, I wag my tail madly and even manage a grin for the man. There, I've obviously done my best to be a credit to my breed by acting friendly, as the man is smiling.

Now I realize we're in a car, and that my human, Mrs. Smell-So-Good, is called Mrs. Susman. I wonder what my name is. And how will I know when we're home?

"Now don't worry, little one," she reassures me, as she carries me out of the car. "We're going into this large condo building. Then we'll take the elevator up to the twenty-third floor, and when we get out, you'll be safe in your new home."

We enter the building, only to have two more men rush out to greet us. It seems there are lots more humans than I knew. I thought it was a dog's world. Maybe the saying "dog eat dog" is why. I wonder if men eat men. Anyway, these men make a big fuss over me, which pleases my human.

We get in another box, only this one is tall and skinny. A door closes and whoosh—we're flying! There's no time to be scared because the door opens almost at once and she carries me into the biggest place I've ever seen. My new home.

Chapter Four

I'm tired and excited all at once. I'm hungry, too. I look at her in my most pleading manner—you know the look—tail wagging, eyes filled with hope. It works.

"I bet you're hungry and tired, little one," she whispers to me. "Let's go in the kitchen. We have a nice comfy place all ready for you."

All the time she's talking, we're heading down this long hall. Her heels clippity-clop on the floor. I've never seen a floor like this. I know about dirt, grass, and carpet, but this floor is smooth and shiny. I can almost recognize my face in it.

Mrs. SSG puts me in a wooden crate with high sides. Then she disappears. I need a nap, but I'm lonesome, worried, and hungry. The crate is too big with just me in it. Ah, she's coming back with a water bowl.

Where is my mother when I need her?

I need milk, not water. Oh, she's holding another dish with a few brown pebbles in the bottom.

"Here, sweetie, here's some water and food. Yum, yum, isn't it good?"

She holds out her hand towards me and one of the brown things is in her palm. It doesn't look good to me, so I turn my head away. Politely, of course. Then I curl up to take a nap. She covers me with a little quilt. It feels warm, but not silky like my mother.

I want my mother.

Dreaming about Classy and my mom, I drift off to sleep.

"Ellen, I'm home."
A deep voice invades my sleep. Then I catch the tread of shoes—it's surely a very large person. The noise is heading straight towards my pen. Who is it? Where is Mrs. Smell-So-Good? I mean, Mrs. Susman. Is she also called Ellen? This is all so confusing. And what's my name?

I hear the lighter patter of her feet, smell her special scent, and now she's opening my crate, talking all the time.

"Oh, Steve, he's just adorable! Wait till you see him."

The big man looms over the crate—his gaze is focused, as though he's inspecting me. Now I see he's not exactly huge, just powerful.

My instinct tells me I'd better please him, or else. I'll do my best.

My lady proudly places me in his arms. I guess he's petting me, but it feels so rough. Not like the lady. I wish he'd do it softer.

"Easy, Steve," she gently instructs Mr. BigGuy. "He's just a puppy. Just stroke him lightly."

Whew, that's better. In fact, it almost feels good. Maybe he can learn. It's apparent that Mrs. SSG really likes this man person. Life in the adopted world is certainly complicated.

Gently she takes me away from the man and places me back in the crate. I obligingly curl up in my favorite sleep position, and Mr. and Mrs. walk out. It feels like bedtime, but after all, I'm only two months old, and I'm homesick. I think about crying, but that may not be wise. I don't want to be sent back. My instincts tell me that would not be appropriate behavior for a well-bred King Charles Cavalier Spaniel.

Without realizing it, I accidentally let out a small whimper—nothing much, just a low cry.

I hear the patter of Mrs.' footsteps.

"What's the matter, sweetie?" she says, as she unlatches the crate. I wag my tail ferociously to let her know how happy I am to see her. But instead of taking me out, she places a round hard thing in my crate. The thing is wrapped in a towel, and makes sort of a tick-tock noise. I wonder why she did that.

And then she closes the door and goes away. Again.

The kitchen is very quiet. Except now there's this thing inside the crate making noise. It's lumpy, and in my way. I don't like this at all.

I must be brave. Everything will be better. I simply have to be brave. But I truly don't feel brave.

I let out a distinct whimper. And another one, only much louder this time. On my third cry, I smell her heading my way. She is walking very fast. Good, maybe I'm going to be rescued. I don't like this crate. I especially don't like being alone.

Chapter Five

Can you believe it? Amazing! Here I am, tucked between the two of them, stretched out on top of what must be the softest blanket in the entire world! This is much better.

I could drift off to sleep now. This is almost like being with my mom and Classy. I feel safe, warm, and protected.

There's only one problem.

He snores.

It sounds a bit like the noise in the kennel. In some ways, it's comforting. But it's so loud that it's hard to fall asleep. At least it seems that way to me. I wonder how she manages. Maybe dogs can hear better than humans.

Look at her, sleeping peacefully. Maybe I can work my way closer to her and slip under the covers.

I'm feeling sleepy—gosh, I wonder what my name is. Maybe it's "Little One"?

Chapter Six

I wake up because I have to go potty. Cautiously I begin wiggling around under the cover. She moves a bit. There, I've got my head out—maybe a small lick on her cheek—oops, too much. Mrs. SSG sits up in surprise.

"Oh, puppy," she says. "You must need to pee."

She flings off the covers, jumps out of bed, and throws on a fluffy long piece of cloth. With a swift movement, she grabs me and heads out the door. Where is the big man? I look around, but we're moving fast down the clickety-clack floor.

I smell fresh air. We must be going outside.

"Steve, I'm taking the puppy out to the terrace." My human tosses this bit of news over her shoulder as she moves closer to the fresh smell.

She swings open a door, and we emerge onto—what did she call it?—a terrace? She sets me down and I trot a few steps. Even though I have to wee right now, I look around. This terrace place is bigger than the exercise pen at my old home. I hear water and see that it's coming out of a strange fish. It makes me really need to pee. But where? There are a few scruffy bushes and flower beds, but there's nothing to hide behind, and there are no odors that tell me it's okay to relieve myself. This is becoming a crisis.

"Go ahead, sweetie, make a tinkle."

What on earth is a tinkle? And where should I go ahead? I can't hold it much longer. This is too much to ask of a puppy. But wait—there's a high fence. Maybe the other side is where I'm supposed to go. I walk over to peek between the bars.

Holy smoke! What a mistake that would've been: It's a million miles down to the dirt. We must be up in the sky. This is scary.

Miss Ellen has been watching me and now she picks me up and places me on a small square of grass. Surely she doesn't expect me to pee? No self-respecting dog, even a puppy, would relieve himself in such an open spot, and especially not a well-bred Cavalier spaniel.

Help me, Mother, what am I to do?

I know. I'll just quietly sidle over behind that water thing, back my fanny up to the bars, and somehow maybe I can pee and it will slide off the side and she won't see.

This isn't working. I can't get my tinkle (well, that's what she called it) to hang over the side. So I'll just squat and pee.

"Good boy, what a good boy. Now let's go have breakfast."

All I did was pee and she's pleased. It doesn't take much to make her happy. Maybe I'll like it here.

Chapter Seven

The past three months have gone by in a whirl. I think I've got the rules down pat for succeeding in the human world, although there's still a lot to learn. It's as simple as **ABC**:

A. Always be friendly.
B. Be careful where you pee and poop.
C. Come when called.

I've made some mistakes but I've learned from them. The most awful lesson happened last week when I was trying to follow the first rule, Rule A, "Always be friendly."

The house was crowded with people—I think it's called a party when you have lots of guests and serve all types of food and drink—and I was a star! Almost everyone, but especially the ones like Mrs. SSG with pretty smells, were making a big fuss over me as I wagged, grinned, and generally tried hard to be sociable. Then I got into BIG trouble.

I don't see why everyone got so upset just because I dropped a poop in the middle of the living room carpet. That's when I learned Rule B.

"Otis!" Mrs. S screamed. *Well, at least now I realize my name is Otis.* "What did you do? BAD BOY!"

With that, she scooped me up (you'd think she'd have scooped the poop up first) and hauled me into the kitchen. I felt really bad. But then Herman tossed me an hors d'oeuvre and my attitude improved slightly. Mrs. SSG was so mad at me. I was in disgrace. Maybe people don't find poops adorable. Dogs don't seem to mind—in fact, I love to smell other dogs' poops. This is another proof that it's not a dog's world—it's a people world. But I want to fit in, so okay, I won't do that again.

I learned Rule C, “Come when called,” the very next day.

When Mr. S and I got up, Mrs. SSG was gone.

“Otey, today we’re going to see Ellen ride in a horse show,” Mr. S told me as he was getting dressed. I wasn’t sure what a horse show was, but I knew the word “go,” and I figured “Otey” was another way of saying my name. I was ready. She’d left for the fairgrounds, but Herman was going to take Mr. and me.

Herman drove us a long, long way. As the car began to slow down, I picked up interesting new smells. It wasn’t just doggy odors, it was something else, too. Herman parked the car and Mr. lifted me out. Then he handed me to Herman, mumbling something about getting a cup of coffee.

"Go find my wife, Herman," he said. "I'll meet you in front of her barn."

He handed me over and turned toward the place where the coffee aroma was coming from. Somehow Herman lost control of the leash, and I was loose!

Taking a last look at Herman, I took off to investigate all the unfamiliar odors. First, I darted under a car to study all the new sights in safety. I saw rows and rows of tents. There were huge animals all over—the biggest creatures I ever saw in my life. And people were on top of them. Out of the corner of my eye, I saw Herman running as fast as he could.

"Otis, where are you?" Herman looked really worried, but I knew I wasn't lost, so I sneaked away again, zipping between cars to stay safe.

I had a wild half hour. I stopped to roll in some horse poop—that's called manure, I found out later. It didn't smell so good, so I won't do that again. Then I saw people eating, so I ducked under the hooves of the big animals and headed into a food tent. A nice man threw me a doughnut. Mmm, that was tasty. A lot better than the brown pebbles I get at home. That's the one area that needs improving in my life. Brown pebbles are boring. I could hear Herman yelling for me which made me feel guilty for not listening, but I was having such a great time.

Then I smelled Ellen, so I raced up to her, because by now I was getting a little worried. After all, I am a King Charles Spaniel. She was standing in front of one of those big animals.

"Otis!" She stared at me in dismay. "Where have you been? What's happened to you? Oh, look at your coat. You're a mess."

I got a spanking for running away. Then I was hosed off with cold water. I didn't like that a bit. I think that next time I'll come when I'm called, but it sure was fun.

When I grow up, maybe I'll write a book for dogs called the Otis ABCs of Social Behavior.

Chapter Eight

One balmy spring morning Ellen decides to take me to the dog park. I have no idea what a dog park is, but then, everything's new when you're a puppy. It turns out to be a large, fenced-in area with benches, sand pits, and lots of low bushes. I am sporting my new leather leash. We walk through the gate and Ellen unsnaps my lead. Now what?

I stay close to her side as she heads for a bench. What I see now is amazing! Dogs of all sizes and shapes dash about, running loose in every direction.

Mrs. SSG settles herself on a bench in the sun.

"There, Otis, now go play," she instructs.

What am I supposed to do?

Uh oh! A HUGE dog is galloping up to me with his teeth bared as though he's going to chomp me to pieces. I cower under Ellen's legs.

"Oh, Otis, oh, my goodness!" Then she lets out a scream.

When he's two feet away, the monster digs his paws in the dirt and stops in his tracks. There we are, nose to nose. I shake but don't move. Not even my eyeballs. Then I get it. He's grinning at me. He wants to be friends. The dog park might be fun. Timidly I wag my tail. He wags his whole body and his tail, and turns over, legs waving madly in the air.

"Look, Otis, what a nice dog." Ellen appears pale but relieved. She pets our new friend who turns out to be a Great Dane named Charlie.

Charlie gets up, shakes the dirt from his coat, and motions for me to come along. I saunter away at his side to check out the place. At least now I have a bodyguard.

I soon learn that Charlie is all bluff and very friendly. He introduces me to his other best buddy. She's even smaller than I am. When she sees Charlie she wags everything she's got. I think she's really cute and I get excited when she's around.

When we get home, Ellen tells Steve that I made friends with a Great Dane named Charlie and a Toy Poodle named Elsie. I had no idea there were so many breeds of dogs. But that's because I'm mostly with people. I wonder if there are lots of breeds of people. I know they come in different colors, but I think they're all still people.

"Ellen," Steve asks, "do they have play groups for the smaller dogs?"

She stands there with her mouth open.

"What a thought! Steve, that's brilliant." Ellen is glowing with excitement. "You endow so many institutions; wouldn't it be nice if you opened a special little park for small dogs?"

Steve looks at Ellen with a strange expression. Then he grins.

"I like that. We can call it the 'Otis Petting Park,' donated by Steve Susman."

Imagine—I'm not even a year old and they're going to name a park after me. My mother will be so proud.

Chapter Nine

I'm one year old, and just as my mother predicted, I understand a lot more now. If sometimes not all the words make sense, the gestures and expressions of humans are usually clear to me. My life is wonderful, filled with love, good care and adventure.

Herman and Lucy help take care of me. Herman walks me sometimes, and he drives the car when we go places. Lucy fills my water dish and cleans my bed. Of course I never stay in my basket—sleeping with my humans is much cozier. But I still don't care for the brown pebbles that are my main meal.

I now know that I live in a condo, ride up and down in an elevator, and have my own name: Otis. I'm housebroken —at least that's what Mrs. SSG proudly tells her friends when they visit. It's a strange way to say I don't mess up the house anymore. Hardly ever.

My family travels a lot. When the valises come out of the closet, and Mrs. SSG is racing around trying on clothes, I know there's a trip coming up. Like right now. She's got three bags laid out on the bed. That means a longer trip. I lie down quietly by the suitcases.

"Don't worry, Otis," she says absent-mindedly, reaching down to pet me. "You're coming along."

She walks into her closet—it's a very big closet—and comes out with my travel bag. Now I know I'm going. I jump up, my tail wags, my ears are almost straight up, and I give my pretend growl. I love that bag. It's jammed with all my things: my favorite rubber pull toy, the soft teddy bear that they throw for me, my dog plate, those little brown pebbles, and my leash.

I've stayed in the best hotels: the Peninsula, the Four Seasons, the Ritz Carlton, and my favorite, the Regency on Park Avenue in New York. Did you know they provide doggie bowls and special treats? That's my home away from home. All the doormen know me, the concierge knows me, and other dogs stay there, too. There's a huge dog in the exact same spot in the lobby all the time, but the funny thing is, he never moves. It's like he's frozen in one spot. I always sniff him and he doesn't smell right. I wonder what kind of dog he is, and how he stands so still all the time.

We're leaving by plane for New York in a few hours. I love flying. Looking out the window I can see the blue sky and the pretty clouds. Sometimes I sleep, stretching out on one of the seats with my favorite comforter. (I admit flying spoils me for other modes of transportation.)

We're going to the City for a few days because Steve is scheduled to speak at a very big school he calls "Yale." A few months ago there was a dinner party at our house and the President of Yale was one of the guests. I hung around and learned a lot. For instance, Yale alumni are called "Eli's."

Steve took me to New Haven to see the campus once and I left my mark on its hallowed ground. Actually, I left several marks. I'm never invited when he speaks anywhere, but some time I'd like to sneak under the seats and hear the big man talk. He's very persuasive, you know.

My man is a Very Important Person. I know that now. Wouldn't people be surprised to see him walking me on the quiet city streets in the morning, carrying a plastic bag to pick up my poop? I must be a VIP, too.

Stacy—Ellen and Mr. Big Man's daughter—lives in the city with her husband, Tom. We're going to their house after the speech. Nicholas lives with them now, too. He's their baby and gets more attention than I do. But that's okay because he's helpless.

When I was three months old I was house trained and could eat by myself and be left alone for hours at a time. He can't do any of that.

Stacy puts him on a blanket on the floor and I get to lick him and sit with him. He's cute and he smells nice. Now Mrs. SSG and Mr. S have other names. Stacy and Tom call them Meme and Poppa. I wonder if I'll ever have another name. Of course, I suppose I already have two, if you count my fancy name.

Chapter 10

The trip to New York was fun. From there we flew to Toronto because Steve has another case—that's lawyer work. Sometimes we live out of suitcases without unpacking them. We're staying at the Four Seasons Resort in Toronto. This is a very posh hotel, and at the risk of sounding smug, I might add that we occupy the presidential suite. I adore all this luxury.

It's 6:30 in the morning, and I have to go out. Mrs. SSG, who always knows what I need, is taking a shower. Mr. Him (who is not quite as reliable, because he's always *thinking*—big lawyer thoughts, I suppose) is sitting on the edge of the bed putting on his shoes. He must have a big case today because he's wearing one of his lawyer suits. (When he's going to the gym he puts on smelly old sweats.)

I wiggle around to get his attention. This is difficult, as his mind is obviously in the courtroom. Doesn't he realize the time? They don't have indoor plumbing for dogs, even in upscale establishments like the Four Seasons, and I need to go out. Come to think of it, I have a brilliant idea! Hotels have bathrooms and powder rooms for their guests. Why can't there be indoor doggie rooms? I wish I could tell my humans. What an obvious improvement for a five-star hotel!

The situation is becoming critical. I whine and wiggle harder, looking at the door anxiously. Finally, the big man notices me.

"Honey, should I take Otis out?" he shouts in the general direction of the bathroom.

"Oh, Steve, that'd be great." Her reply is muffled, but Mr. Big Man gets the idea.

"Come on, Otis, let's fasten your lead and get going. I wouldn't mind a cup of coffee anyhow. Let's go, boy."
Mr. Him opens the door and we head down the hall towards the elevator. Relief is in sight. Happily I bounce along next to Mr. Him. We leave the elevator, cross the lobby, and head for a little park near the hotel. Then, after I've taken care of necessities, Mr. Him buys a cup of coffee at Starbucks, and we go back to the hotel.

The elevator is crowded—we step in, and the car starts to rise. We're going to the twenty-fourth floor, so Mr. Him buries his nose in the newspaper, which he's holding in his right hand, and dangles my leash in his left hand. I am watching the little red light in the elevator that signals up, up, up.

The elevator stops, and a nice looking lady smiles at me and gets out. I take the smile as an invitation and trot out behind her. The elevator door closes and the next thing I know, I'm dangling in the air, hanging by my tattered old lead. I can't breathe! I'm choking!

Meanwhile, Mr. Him must still be in the elevator engrossed in reading the paper, holding the leash.

When the car slows, he looks down. I'm not there. Just a frayed end of a lead, with no dog attached.

"My God, I've hung the dog!" he shouts, his eyes wide. "Stop the elevator!"

By now the nice lady on the twenty-third floor hears me gasping for breath as I dangle by my collar, three feet off the floor. Quickly she reaches out to hold me, and as she does, the lead snaps. The nice lady hugs and pets me. I'm sniffling, although now that I can breathe again, I feel okay. I can't help thinking how smart I was to use the leather lead as a teething tool. If I hadn't been gnawing away at the leash for the past week, it might not have snapped. Why, I could still be dangling in the air!

At the same time, Steve races down the hall to the suite. Banging on the door, he shouts, “Honey, I’ve killed Otis!”

Mrs. SSG, hearing the panic in Steve’s voice, flings on her bathrobe and ties the sash as she opens the door. There stands Steve.

“I don’t know what happened. One minute there he was, sitting quietly at my feet in the elevator, and the next thing I knew he was gone, and all I had was a piece of the lead.” Steve is speaking so quickly, he barely makes sense, but Ellen gets it.

“I’ll go down to the lobby,” Ellen says decisively. “Maybe someone has him. Surely they’ll turn him in at the desk.”

Ellen races out of the suite, leaving Steve pacing up and down.

As she gets off the elevator, Mrs. SSG spies a small group of people gathered at the concierge's desk. They are surrounding a tall lady holding a small dog (me). I am lapping up the attention, but when I see how upset Mrs. SSG seems, I let my ears droop—just a tad.

"Oh, Otey," Ellen cries. "Are you okay?"

Turning to the lady, she holds out her arms, and I am safe at last with Mrs. SSG.

"Thank you so much, we can't thank you enough," she babbles to my rescuer.

No doubt about it, this little adventure has been the height of excitement. And I do mean height. But, hey, all's well that ends well—and I bet they'll give me a special treat to make me feel better.

Chapter Eleven

Mrs. SSG and I just landed in Florida—at least that's what Gerald said. The warm air is a bit like my home town, but a little different. I think I'll pee on the tree with the sticky looking leaves. We don't have this kind of tree in Houston.

Carefully, I skirt the tree before relieving myself. Ellen waits while I investigate the smells.

"C'mon, Otis," Mrs. SSG says, "It's time to visit my mom and Aubrey."

We hop in the waiting car and after a short ride we stop in front of a large house surrounded by trees so tall I can't see the tops of them. Mrs. SSG opens the car door and I'm excited by the doggie odors that even my unsophisticated pug nose can't miss. Eagerly I race around the big front lawn, following the scents to the front door.

The door opens, and a big man walks out and gives Mrs. SSG a warm bear hug. That's fine, but then a huge dog runs out with the man, obviously planning to bite me into two pieces. I freeze. I mean freeze.

"Champ, be nice," says the large man to the big dog, reaching down to pet me. "Champ—behave yourself. Otis is a nice puppy."

The dog doesn't look quite as big now that he's not lunging towards me. His tail is wagging but he's still so pushy, sniffing me all over, especially my private parts. I have my hands full trying not to offend this big guy. I don't want to fight. I never want to fight. I'm a lover.

Now another dog is waddling out of the house. Or is it a dog? Smells like one, but it looks more like a large black sausage with legs. Think I'll sniff it. Maybe it's a strange form of cat.

Champ lets out a warning growl just as I get near the sausage, so I quickly back away and lick the big dog instead. Surely he knows I only want to be friendly.

Meanwhile Ellen's mom is hugging her. It's really a mushy scene. Mrs. SSG likes the two dogs, too, and she's petting them and loving them up. I'm not jealous, at least not too much.

We go into the house with Champ leading the way and the little thing (they call her "Dolly") tags along at his heel. I follow sedately. No sense getting into trouble now. Champ heads left, toward the kitchen. (I can always tell a kitchen because of the odors.) There are two large bowls filled to the brim with food that smells a lot more interesting than my brown pebbles. I better be polite and not try any, but it looks like real food. Champ takes a few bites, then Dolly nudges her way in front of him and the most amazing thing happens: He backs away, gives her a big slurp on the neck and lets her have the bowl all to herself. That bowl is larger than she is—she could sleep in it! Dolly looks like a puppy but acts old. Maybe she's Champ's puppy. But she has no teeth.

Now Champ gives me a signal and I follow him as he runs to another room. All of a sudden, he disappears. He went through a door with a flap on it and, oh my goodness, he's on the outside of the house. I watch him, not sure what to do. Ellen goes through the real door and calls me.

"Come on, Otey," she coaxes. "You can do it. Come on through the dog door just like Champ." She's holding a treat in her hand, but I'm still not sure about the flap on the opening.

Champ comes back in, and then goes out again. He's actually grinning at me. Oh, I see, he's trying to show me how to go through the wall. Well, a King Charles Spaniel ought to be able to do what he did—so here goes.
Gritting my teeth, I push the flap aside and bound through the dog door, my heart doing bang-bangs.

“Good boy, Otis,” Mrs. SSG says, clapping her hands. ”Now you can play in the yard with Champ and Dolly.”

Funny—no one praised Champ.

The humans are on the porch, talking while they watch us play. Champ lets me nuzzle the Dolly dog. It is a dog, after all, just a funny looking little thing. After a while we’re thirsty, so Champ leads us back through the door flap.

Then my eyes nearly pop out of my head. The humans have tossed food scraps into three doggie dishes. (I guess they put one extra down for me.) Potatoes, and steak—this is unbelievable. No pebbles. I eat until I’m ready to burst, then lie down quietly next to Mrs. SSG. As I drift off to sleep, I can’t help thinking sometimes I’d like to be a little less royal.

Chapter Twelve

I've finally figured out that we're a doggy family. Ellen's folks have Champ, which they call a Belgian Malinois, and Dolly, the sausage, is a Mini Dachshund. Stacy and Tom have Nicholas, but he's a human baby, not a dog. Still, he's fun.

Now I have a new cousin, a dog named Oscar. He belongs to Harry, Mrs. SSG and Mr. Big Man's son, and Karen, his wife. Oscar is fancy, just like me. He's a Dogue de Bordeaux. As a puppy, Oscar was just my size—for about a week. Now he weighs 150 pounds. He's supposed to herd sheep, or something. Of course Harry and Karen don't have any sheep in their house, so basically he just eats and drools.

I like to stick my head down Oscar's throat. It's amazing what you can see in there. Oscar doesn't mind. Last week Harry had a birthday party for him. Lots of dogs came and it was like a circus. We played dunking for hot dogs, Frisbee fetch, and ended with a great big birthday cake. The affair was catered by Three Dog Bakery. I love real food.

Tomorrow we leave for Aspen. It's so different from Houston—I love the snow, being outside, and hiking. We have a large house in Aspen on top of a mountain and you can see forever. I'm supposed to be careful so no bear or other big animal grabs me, but I'm not sure what to look for, so I just play and explore, and the people watch out for me.

I have to go now. You see, Steve's been in Alaska working on a very big case for over two months, and he's lonesome. Of course Mrs. SSG flies up to visit him for a week at a time, but sometimes she has other obligations here in the States and can't get away.

And he wants me to come to Alaska to keep him company. Can you imagine? I sure have come a long way with someone who doesn't like pets so much. But the fact is that I love Steve, too. I wonder if I need a coat. I hear that it's cold in Alaska.

It's been arranged: Tomorrow Jim and Gerald are going to fly me up in our jet so I can keep the big man company. Just me and Steve.

Maybe when I'm in Alaska I will meet some sled dogs.

Mush, everybody.

ACKNOWLEDGEMENTS

My "pawmanship" leaves a lot to be desired, so a special thank you to Mrs. SSG's mom, Babette Williams, for translating my story into people-speak.

The photo of me on the cover is a copy of an original oil painting by Billy Sullivan.

The photo of Mrs. SSG's mom on the back cover was taken by Merle Kuns. Susan K. Perry edited the book, and Aubrey Williams was a first-rate cheering section.

To all, my deepest appreciation.

Otis

Printed in the United States
49583LVS00001B/259-522

9 781589 398627